WATFORD
1347

INTRODUCING QUALITY ASSURANCE
INTO THE NHS

INTRODUCING QUALITY ASSURANCE INTO THE NHS

Practical Experience from Wandsworth Continuing Care Unit

TERRY GOULD
Unit General Manager
Continuing Care Unit
Wandsworth Health Authority
St George's Hospital, Wandsworth, London

and

HILARY MERRETT
Hospital/Business Manager
Wandsworth Health Authority
Bolingbroke Hospital
Wandsworth Common, London

M
MACMILLAN

First published 1992 by
THE MACMILLAN PRESS LTD
Houndmills, Basingstoke, Hampshire RG21 2XS
and London
Companies and representatives
throughout the world

ISBN 0-333-57061-8

Printed in China

A catalogue record for this book is available from the
British Library

Contents

Foreword

I welcome the opportunity to write the Foreword to this innovative document. It is in keeping with both the Citizen's and Patient's Charters. I have often heard people remark that we are a passive nation, but in these days there is a growing awareness of consumer rights, and people's expectations for high standards of service are, quite rightly, increasing.

The Government's reforms will not only ensure that money follows patients, but also that services are provided where the patients need them. Quality of care must play a vital role in this, and publications such as this one will help to ensure that even faster progress is made.

I hope that it will find wide support throughout the NHS.

Right Honourable Baroness Julia Cumberlege
Parliamentary Under Secretary of State for Health

Acknowledgements

This book would not have been possible without the help and support of all the staff of the Continuing Care Unit, Wandsworth Health Authority, who enthusiastically developed the quality approach which we have attempted to describe.

We would especially like to thank James Barnard for his cartoons, Pat Spooner, Professional Development Officer, Sharon Phillips who was responsible for the training programmes, and Irene Goring and Susan Bishara for their work on patient satisfaction.

Finally, we would like to thank Ursula Stevenson, Monica Storey and Maria Crockford who laboriously typed out our scribbled words.

Introduction

'... A man's reach should exceed his grasp or what's a heaven for?'

Browning

There is a dichotomy about the concept of quality which underpins the account in this book of how health service managers can translate good quality service provision from words into action. Much of the recent academic work on quality in health care has centred on the need to set achievable and measurable standards and it is rapidly becoming even more important to establish such measures in the trading environment of the 1990s as the contractual process evolves. In order to make any new and significant achievement, however, there is a need for a more inspirational force and the drawing out of the human instinct to strive for the ideal, even for the unattainable ... to go for gold.

This book charts the efforts of a small health service unit in an inner London Health Authority to find a balance between a structured and comprehensive approach to quality health care management and the revelation that a little bit of imagination and enterprise can go a long way.

The Continuing Care Unit of Wandsworth Health Authority provided health care services for the community, for elderly people and those with learning difficulties. Services for the elderly are based at the Bolingbroke Hospital, a 103-bedded unit for acute geriatric patients.

That the theoretical and practical approaches can go hand in hand has been illustrated by the Unit's success in winning the Sunday Times Best of Health award for best community hospital of 1989 for the Bolingbroke Hospital.

In her introduction to the report of the competition[1], Tessa Brooks, Director of Quality Assurance, King's Fund Centre, identified the key distinction between defining quality in industry and in the public service. In industry the customers' requirements are paramount but in the NHS the provider is the arbiter of quality care. To

1

A. Donabedian's three parts of quality assurance in health care[2]—good clinical care, good relationships between carers and patients, and good environment—Brooks adds the integration of activity with the goals of the organisation and the aspiration to achieve. We hope to demonstrate how to put these principles into practice.

Although we do not see it as the purpose of this book to join the debate on the definition of quality in health care, Brooks has made two statements which seem to us to encompass both the practice and the theory of what we have tried to do:

' The secret of quality is in a careful matching of the care required by patients with the capacity of its providers ...'

and

'... quality is a moving target ... (perhaps) imperfectly achieved.'

The pursuit of quality in health care is now no longer merely desirable for managers; it is essential if hospitals and other facilities providing health services in the 1990s are to remain viable. The Citizen's Charter initiatives have helped to focus management effort on achieving improvements to services for individuals. The implementation of the Patient's Charter from April 1992 provides the impetus not only to tackle the big issues of waiting lists and times, but also to examine the accessibility and acceptability of the service we offer. These are quality issues: we hope the Patient's Charter will become integral to quality programmes rather than the sole motivating force. The purpose of this account is to show how the concept of quality can be assimilated into the culture of an organisation by establishing a commitment to its most precious resource—people.

1   Putting quality into practice

Communication—the key to quality

When the Continuing Care Unit launched its quality programme in 1987, the issue was not so much one of initiating developments as recognising and publicising work already underway. It must be very rare for any organisation to start from scratch when looking at how to provide a quality service, and, indeed, any attempt to do so—to impose quality—may demotivate and alienate the very people on whom the project will rely.

The task for the unit was, therefore, to establish an atmosphere of trust among all the staff; an environment where people could feel comfortable and cared for, and where it was worth striving for high standards of care.

Model or motivation?

A formal quality model was seen as important but only part of the total approach to the subject. There are several essential elements of any quality programme:

- it must facilitate action
- it must produce standards which can be defined, communicated, achieved and monitored
- it must become integral to the organisation and the delivery of services rather then being imposed on the existing structure
- everyone within the organisation must understand and accept their role within the programme

Work began immediately on defining the goals of the Unit and its care groups: services for elderly people, for people with learning difficulties and community services. An intensive programme of quality group meetings with nurses began in 1988, looking at the goals and principal functions of each group of nurses (health visitors, school nurses, district nurses, ward sisters etc.). Over the past few years, this exercise has been extended to all disciplines of staff. The approach is based on Chris Wilson's quality model[3] and leads to standard-setting by each group of staff across the whole range of services.

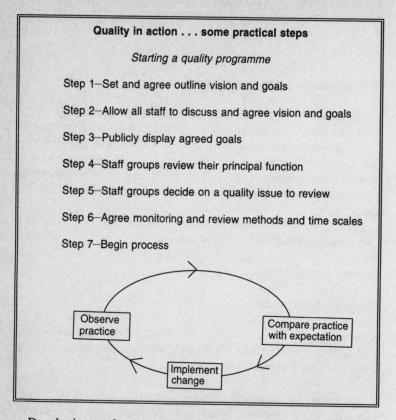

Quality in action . . . some practical steps

Starting a quality programme

Step 1—Set and agree outline vision and goals

Step 2—Allow all staff to discuss and agree vision and goals

Step 3—Publicly display agreed goals

Step 4—Staff groups review their principal function

Step 5—Staff groups decide on a quality issue to review

Step 6—Agree monitoring and review methods and time scales

Step 7—Begin process

Observe practice

Compare practice with expectation

Implement change

Developing goal statements and agreeing principal functions and achievable standards is a time-consuming but rewarding task which is still in progress at the time of writing. There is certainly no need to wait for the identification of goals at all levels before establishing a dynamic quality programme.

Once the ultimate standard was set—the continuing commitment of senior management to the vision of the organisation and to the care of its staff—work could begin and, most importantly, existing good practice and potential could be recognised and given a chance to develop within the quality structure.

The vision of the unit and its goals were crystallised into a statement which was agreed with all staff—to provide and promote a high standard of health care in order to improve the quality of life, within the resources available, in ways which are accepted by the people of Wandsworth. The aim is to:

- establish and maintain mutual trust throughout the unit
- encourage the client/carer/relative to share decisions on the choice of treatment and care
- influence other organisations to promote good health in their values and beliefs
- encourage good internal communications
- actively recognise the importance of the contribution made by each member of staff
- evaluate current activities in terms of the expectations of patients/carers/relatives acceptable professional standards and managerial goals
- encourage and empower all staff to maintain and pursue the highest standards of care
- ensure that staff at all levels are able to put forward ideas and express creativity and initiative
- recognise and develop good practice

Getting started—a framework for quality

In order to monitor the programme and establish it as central to the agenda of senior management, a formal structure was devised reflecting those issues which are essential for the achievement of the Unit's stated objectives. The responsibility for quality throughout the Unit was therefore placed in five main groups: clinical standards, physical environment, patient satisfaction, staff development, and customer relations. Each group was chaired by a member of the Unit Management Board and reported back monthly to the Board's meetings. A complaints monitoring group was also established as an extra 'arm' to the patient satisfaction group, reporting to the Board on the handling of complaints in the Unit and with a brief to prepare a good-practice checklist for complaints management.

It will be immediately obvious that there are considerable areas of overlap between these groups. This was recognised from the beginning and a representative from one group would attend another where issues concerned both groups, thus ensuring as little duplication of effort as possible. To a certain extent the service has now outgrown these original groupings and work is under way to adjust the structure so that it reflects, and is able to monitor, the development of quality initiatives.

5

The important point is, however, to set up a system which can facilitate action. If that means, in practice, that the division of responsibilities is not always strictly logical, neat or tidy, so be it. Provided that people know their remit and ultimate goals, then each group is free to pursue those goals in its own style. The clinical standards group, for example, looked at immunisation services in the light of Robert Maxwell's six quality criteria[4]:

- acceptability
- equity
- appropriateness
- efficiency
- effectiveness
- accessibility

These criteria form an invaluable starting point for the monitoring of the quality of service provision.

The Unit General Manager appointed the chair of each of the five working groups and asked that the membership should be representative of as many different staff groups as possible. Each group was given a brief to draw up a quality assurance programme in its area defined as follows:

- Clinical standards—the awareness of patients' well-being
- Patient satisfaction—the awareness of response
- Customer relations—the awareness of customers' vulnerability and position
- Staff satisfaction and development—the awareness of staff needs
- Physical environment—the awareness of responsibility for the bricks and mortar of health care and its importance to the needs of patients, clients and staff

Lists of related topics were identified for each group; some attained more importance than others, some diminished, and many others were added, and are still being added, as the search for the best in quality health care continues.

In the following chapters, the developing remit of each group is discussed and illustrated with examples from the work of the unit. Some of these examples are the result of a formal quality assurance programme, others may be seen more as a result of the growth of a commitment of all the staff to providing top quality service.

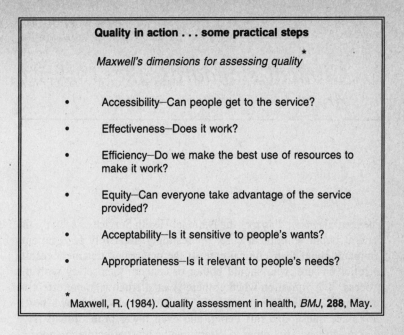

Quality in action . . . some practical steps

Maxwell's dimensions for assessing quality[*]

- Accessibility—Can people get to the service?

- Effectiveness—Does it work?

- Efficiency—Do we make the best use of resources to make it work?

- Equity—Can everyone take advantage of the service provided?

- Acceptability—Is it sensitive to people's wants?

- Appropriateness—Is it relevant to people's needs?

[*] Maxwell, R. (1984). Quality assessment in health, *BMJ*, **288**, May.

2 Clinical standards—the work we do

The central *raison d'être* of the National Health Service as seen by the general public is clinical care. Interestingly, relatively few patients complain about their clinical care. If the prescribed treatment results in relief or cure, who should bother or concern themselves with the process? Why question whether there is an alternative, more effective or efficient method of treatment? 'The doctor always knows best!' Few have questioned this belief, and even fewer professionals have ever questioned each other to determine the most effective methods of treatment and care.

One of the few unchallenged aspects of the National Health Service reforms is the requirement to introduce a comprehensive system of medical audit. Considerable sums of money are being made available to medical staff for the purchase of computers and software to ensure that the process gets under way. Some staff have readily seized, or been given, the opportunity to purchase computers and employ additional staff before actually deciding what medical audit is and what it should aim to achieve. Before further sums of money are spent on 'high-tech' equipment, there needs to be clarity about what medical audit actually means and how it can be used to benefit the service.

What is 'audit'?

'Audit' literally means an examination. An examination by itself can be a pointless exercise unless one is prepared to draw conclusions from the examination as to whether, or how, the outcome can be improved. Generally, the outcome of any process can be improved by a modification to that process.

Such necessary modification or change requires agreement by everyone involved in the process followed by its implementation. After a prescribed time, an audit is again conducted and the cycle is repeated. Audit, agreed change and implementation, is a cyclical process which aims to improve practice and thereby the outcome. An endpoint is never reached as there will always be room for improvement.

Audit can be applied to all component parts of the delivery of health care. Jason Brice, in *Management in Medicine* (1989)[5], has broken this down into the following three main groups:

- *Outcome Audit* reports what happens to the patient as a result of an episode of health care. It is the area of greatest interest to the clinicians, the patient and the community at large, but it is the most difficult audit process to implement as it may involve the follow-up of patients for long periods of time.
- *Process Audit* makes an assessment of the delivery of health care as it is carried out. This is a very important part of clinical audit.
- *Resource Audit* gives an assessment of what is put into the system in the way of buildings, money, consumables and staff.

Brice states that clinicians will not have a keen interest in the resource component of audit. However, the authors feel that clinicians must be involved in the management of resources, as these directly influence the quality of care.

Outcome audit and process audit are the key elements of medical and clinical audit. Ideally, outcome and process audit should be multidisciplinary. It can be argued that certain aspects of process audit, such as surgical and nursing procedures, should be accomplished on a unidisciplinary basis, but where the process involves a number of disciplines then the audit of that process must be multidisciplinary. The success of any operation will be influenced by the anaesthetic, the recovery, the post-operative nursing and physiotherapy care. Each of these professions have a direct influence on the eventual outcome. In some instances this care will extend into the community, so there may be good reasons to include the general practitioners, the district nurse and other community staff in this process—the continuity of care, or its absence, will have a direct effect on eventual outcome.

The field of geriatric medicine offers a good example of the need for multidisciplinary audit. The elderly usually present with multiple pathology requiring both health and social care. A number of disciplines play a role in improving the patient's condition to the point of discharge from hospital and on to supporting care in the patient's home. Each hospital-based discipline has to integrate its component of care into a precisely organised framework, or package, to ensure that the rehabilitation process is co-ordinated, so that when discharged from hospital, the patient can be satisfactorily cared for in the community. The decision to discharge a patient should be multidisciplinary and should involve not only those who have been involved in the hospital care, but also those who will continue to care for the patient in the home. Quality delivery of health care with an acceptable outcome depends upon a team approach.

Brice makes an important comment regarding the widespread view that computers and appropriate software are essential in order to audit. He says that this is only partially true as he and many others have carried out effective audit for many years using simple manual methods. It is time consuming but nevertheless possible. It has even been possible, for example, to determine readmission rates and the reasons for increases in these rates. More detailed information will nevertheless be required to audit other aspects of care and outcome. The point is that manual systems can be a good starting point for giving users the opportunity to gain a clearer view of the information and data needed to assess performance by automated methods. It is certainly less threatening to staff to introduce the audit process gradually by using manual systems and ensuring the staff's involvement in the decision-making process surrounding the development of audit systems. The Confidential Enquiry into Perioperative Deaths[6] relied solely on manual reporting and has been used to good effect to highlight the causes of increased perioperative mortality and has led to improvements in practice. The Confidential Enquiry into Maternal Deaths[7], carried out on a three yearly basis, is another example of how manual reporting can be used to audit practice and influence change.

Often small groups of clinicians have agreed among themselves long lists of data without having any view as to how they can use them to audit their quality of clinical care. Anaesthetists can quite happily collect data pertaining to the seniority of the anaesthetist, the operation, the seniority of the surgeon, the premedication, the induction and maintenance agents, the endotracheal tube, the ventilator, the IV cannulae, and the length of time spent in the theatre and recovery ward, without considering a visit to the ward to assess the patient's post-operative well-being. None of the above information

11

is of any real significance, other than to assess the use of resources, if the measures of outcome are not decided first. The importance of establishing the objectives of the exercise (in this case deciding what constitutes a desirable outcome) is central to all systems design and implementation (see Chapter 7 on Information), otherwise the imposition of this data collection on others becomes a threat and leads to suspicion and non-co-operation. Implementation will then be surely doomed to failure. Time should be taken to involve all staff. It is wise to begin with a fairly simple subject to audit, such as catheter care, and obtain the entire staff's commitment to the study, and their agreement as to what data will be required to carry this out, and collect it manually first, as there will undoubtedly be another piece of information which will be found to be significant at a later date. The staff should find this approach less threatening and will then be committed to following it through.

Much current work in medical audit centres on clinical notes and good records management is thus essential to the audit process. By 'records management', we mean the practice of creating and maintaining legible, concise and accurate notes. Recent legislation (the Data Protection Act (1974) and the Access to Health Records Act (1990)) has made this practice a statutory requirement. Recent developments in thinking have led us to recognise the rights of patients in all aspects of their care and treatment, and the concomitant duty on clinicians to consider the wishes and feelings of their patients when writing about them can only be helpful in raising the quality of the service delivered to the public. Clinicians should now more than ever be alert to the misunderstandings that time-honoured phrases such as 'poor historian' and 'pleasant, talkative lady' can cause.

The implications for information technology and for confidentiality are examined in the chapter on information; the salient point about good record keeping with regard to audit processes is that establishing good practice among clinicians, together with an appreciation of the rights of the patient or client, will remove some of the possible obstacles to retrieval and use of clinical data for audit.

The introduction of clinical audit can be a lengthy process. It is essential that all members of the team feel happy in the multidisciplinary setting and overcome any discomfort that may be experienced in an environment of peer review. It can be threatening, but it is of paramount importance that an atmosphere is created where the team members feel equal and are free to question other team members. It is likely that professions which are small in number will feel overshadowed by the larger disciplines, therefore it is recommended that the multidisciplinary teams should be kept small so that the feeling of being outnumbered or overshadowed is minimised. The possible dominance of the consultant must be overcome in order to enable effective multidisciplinary analysis. This may be achieved by encouraging a particularly consultant who accepts the multidisciplinary concept, or by enlisting a consultant who leads the team by seeking others' views and opinions. In other cases it may be achieved by a staged process of involving only two disciplines and gradually including others.

It is probably better for the audit group to focus firstly on issues which do not directly challenge the clinical practice of one team member. For example, issues such as the discharge policy and its effect on outcome. This kind of subject can emphasise the importance of each team member's contribution towards establishing an effective discharge and ensuring against any possible snag in rehabilitation or, at the worst, a readmission. Unlike some other aspects of clinical care, such as drug therapy or surgical procedure as already outlined, a discharge policy cannot be successfully operated by one professional, so this is a good starting point for multidisciplinary audit.

Once the team concept is established and all members of the team feel comfortable and valued, it will then be possible to extend the auditing process to more contentious issues which require careful and detailed appraisal. Several examples of the interplay of different disciplines in the treatment of patients and of this interplay on the eventual outcome are described by Jane Mallett[8].

She cites several examples which highlight the importance of auditing the work of the whole of the health care team. The audit carried out by one group of professionals can appear to be good, but the outcome can be altered dramatically by a change in practice outside of that profession's influence. For example, the surgical process of upper abdominal surgery might appear to be good on audit, but the outcome for the patient can be poor if the physiotherapist fails in his or her responsibility to ensure the patient breathes deeply and secretions are cleared. Similarly, the outcome can be less than satisfactory if the nurse fails to notify the surgeons when there is a haematoma formation under the wound which subsequently becomes infected leading to a wound dehiscence.

This example illustrates the interplay of health professionals in the quality of outcome, that is also influenced by the patient himself. For instance, he or she must be warned to report certain occurrences, such as symptoms of unwanted side-effects of drug therapy or untoward incidents such as post-operative bleeding. As in all aspects of quality assurance, the patient has an important role in the eventual outcome and one should consider where the patient should be included in the

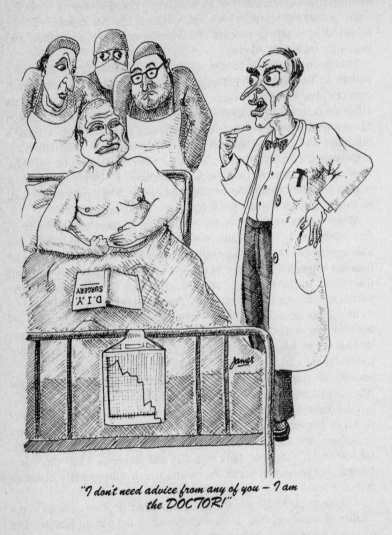

"I don't need advice from any of you — I am the DOCTOR!"

clinical audit process.

The bringing together of all professionals in the team will ensure that every aspect of the care process is audited and changes in practice are monitored against the eventual outcome. By these methods, clear standards of quality (such as protocols for the treatment of varicose ulcers, respiratory complaints, etc.), can be agreed and set by the team. These standards can then be monitored for effectiveness by the panel by measuring changes in outcome. Standards can be suitably modified as a result of practice and further measurement, so fitting into the established cycle of change, implementation, measurement and on to further change.

The successful implementation of clinical audit will not be achieved overnight. Indeed, success in even a limited way depends on the recognition that it is an extension of an existing process and not a new exercise which is imposed. Medical opposition to the ongoing development of medical audit in Canada and the United States testifies to the demotivating effect of such an approach. Clinical audit must be allowed to evolve and develop in the same way as other quality assurance programmes. The place in this process of all health personnel, and of patients and relatives themselves, must be acknowledged. The success of the programme will be judged against improved standards of care and outcome whereas neglect of audit may not inevitably lead to poor outcome but will certainly ensure that desirable outcome cannot be identified, encouraged or reviewed. The desirable outcome we will be endeavouring to achieve will be acceptable to, and effective for, the patient, and demonstrably efficient in resource terms for the health service.

3 Customer relations—dealing with people

The patient as a person

It is incumbent on all health service staff to be both committed and responsive to meeting the physical, emotional and social needs of clients and patients. A friendly, helpful, attentive and caring approach by the health professional and other health service personnel can easily overcome the fear, anxiety and apprehension of the patient. Such an approach will help to establish a relationship which is trusting, and promotes confidence and high expectation. It has been assumed by some that these factors can actually accelerate recovery or improve the outcome of disease. Whether they actually influence outcome will continue to be conjectural, but it is indisputable that the course of an illness becomes more bearable to both its sufferer and relatives if the professional care and support is given in a kind and personal manner. It is far too easy to treat the disease while ignoring the patient. A recent survey within Wandsworth[9] has shown that, although patients are full of praise for the clinical care, they are far more likely to criticise all other aspects of the service provided in hospitals and clinics.

For too long, in the effort to strive for efficiency and reduce costs, there has been a tendency to overlook or ignore the fact that patients are people. When people are ill and seek health care they are vulnerable. Understanding and consideration are essential. Illness does not take away one's right to be treated as a person first. Too often, though, it goes hand in hand with the loss of name and identity, which are substituted by either a bed number or disease category. The combination of illness and institutionalisation can only increase levels of stress for the patient. The person must always come first. The illness or other health need must be recognised as of secondary importance: it is what motivates that person to seek help.

Our 'customers', whether patients, clients, relations or our own

17

staff, have the right to be treated with respect and courtesy. They have the right to know, understand and be able to influence decisions regarding their care and treatment. Any decision of choice of treatment must remain with the patient. The health professional has the responsibility and duty to ensure that the patient and relatives are given the information on which to make that choice in a clear, meaningful and sympathetic way. Sadly, a number of these aspects of customer relations have been overlooked or neglected within the health service in recent years, but there is now a well-established and a growing demand for a consumer-orientated service. This demand will lead to a focusing of attention on improving and reinforcing relationships in the future. Bringing this about in an organisation as labyrinthine and hierarchical as the NHS may seem difficult but the effort is worthwhile, and the rewards of good customer relations benefit the provider of health care just as much as the recipients.

In the new arena of providers and purchasers of health care, those hospitals or units or general practices which boast good customer relations, and hence a favourable public image, will become more marketable and enjoy a distinct advantage when patient preference begins to influence the placing of contracts.

More immediate is the emerging place of GP fundholders within the internal market. In a study of factors likely to affect GP referral behaviour carried out in Bury and North Manchester in 1990[10], GPs ranked the importance of a patient's wishes in favour of a particular hospital or consultant in second place behind the GP's opinion of a consultant's medical knowledge or ability. A patient's negative attitude about a particular hospital also appears in the seven most important factors found to influence a GP's choice of consultant. In the same study, patients themselves listed facilities and equipment, length of waiting times and lists, and the friendliness of staff among the top ten pieces of information they would most like out of a possible twenty-four.

There is a need to provide improved information to the public and to other providers of health care. Some hospitals have taken the lead and distribute regular information sheets to the public. In our Unit, we followed this lead and circulated a General Practitioner Factsheet about hospital services every three months and one-off bulletins about changes in services, retirements, and so on, as and when required. All staff should understand that they have a role in ensuring good communications.

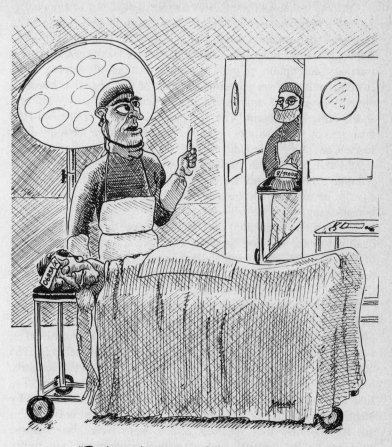

"*Right number 0685 A/X is ready. Now wheel in
the left hip — number 00426 B Type A*"

Customer relations

How can customer relations programmes be introduced and promoted within the health service?

Customer relations must be seen as an essential part of any quality assurance programme and, therefore, will be one of the touchstones to be taken into account in developing a goal or mission statement. The Robert Maxwell dimension of acceptability probably gives the best summary description of good customer relations. Of course, good customer relations are jeopardised if any of the other five Maxwell dimensions—equity, appropriateness, efficiency, effectiveness and accessibility—are absent. The acceptability of any service will be measured by its sensitivity to the needs and wishes of the individual. In the Continuing Care Unit, we took the view that the consumer has a right to expect certain standards. These include freedom of choice, personal service, respect for privacy, and opinion, and, above all, a right to be treated with the everyday courtesy that one expects as a human being.

The mission statement of the Unit, which appears in Chapter 1, was qualified by the wording 'in ways which are accepted by the people of Wandsworth'. This acceptability can be judged by the scrutiny of regular customer feedback. How this can be obtained is discussed in Chapter 4 concerning patient satisfaction.

Once the staff agreed with the overall aim of the Unit, quality groups were established through consultation as described earlier. Membership of these groups was publicised and then we embarked on a steady introduction of customer relations training packages. The content of these packages was fairly simple but required sensitive handling in the breaking down of past practices and prejudices. The first hurdle to be cleared was to ensure access to the services by identifying staff clearly and giving our 'customers' the confidence to ask for any help they required. Simple signs were placed at the entrances to the hospital, and out-patient departments and health clinics, which said: 'Welcome to the . . . . . . The staff are at your service. If you should require any assistance, please do not hesitate to ask at the Reception or any member of staff'.

The introduction of these signs broke the ice and very soon staff started to come forward in anticipation of the patients' or relatives' requests. Staff began to appreciate and take pride in their front-line role. Of course it was imperative that they received adequate training to enable them to cope with the varying demands of the patients and their visitors. All grades of front-line staff attended customer awareness courses which were planned with help from all disciplines of professional and managerial staff. In this way we could ensure that all staff were involved in discussions about effective communication with the public. The portering staff, being at the very sharp end of the interface with the public, were taken through a development programme with the aim of producing the 'good hospital porter' of the 1990s. The programme included topics ranging from lifting and wheelchair handling to communication skills. It is essential that such staff can be easily identified by the customer, so uniforms and clear name-badges were provided.

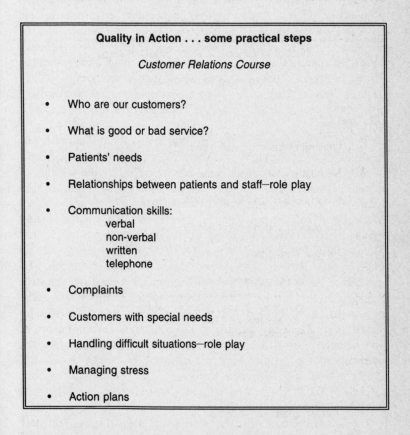

Quality in Action . . . some practical steps

Customer Relations Course

- Who are our customers?

- What is good or bad service?

- Patients' needs

- Relationships between patients and staff—role play

- Communication skills:
    verbal
    non-verbal
    written
    telephone

- Complaints

- Customers with special needs

- Handling difficult situations—role play

- Managing stress

- Action plans

The written word is also a very effective means of communication, and well produced information pamphlets promote good customer relations. In-patient and out-patient booklets were designed in a hospital style and are reviewed biannually for relevance and clarity. Maps and diagrams are provided to make a trip to, or stay in, hospital less bewildering. Clear signposting is required in all hospitals to ensure that sick or disabled patients are not inconvenienced and placed under greater stress by needless walking. It should also be remembered that, even when the needs of a multiracial society have been recognised by the publication of booklets in several languages, the service is pointless if direction signs are not easily understood. It is also worth noting that the friendliest, most helpful member of staff, who stops to help a confused visitor, will be less than effective without a thorough knowledge of the hospital. The importance of staff development and commitment is examined later in Chapter 5.

Quality in action . . . some practical steps

Improving communications

External

- General practitioner newsletters

- Newsletters for general public

- Profiles of services for public reference

- Out-patient and in-patient handbooks

- Regular meetings:

  clinical meetings for GPs
  'get to know your consultant' groups for GPs
  pensioner groups, disability groups, etc.
  Social services, LMC, FHSA
  Voluntary agencies

Internal

- Newsletters

- Annual report

- Regular meetings with all staff

- Heads of departments meetings

- Management on foot

"Ah, yes, Crocus ward . . . first right or is it left, then three doors to your left, straight on through two or it could be three sets of swing doors and ask again. . . ."

The use of photographs of ward staff and managers will often allay the anxiety of patients and help to establish good relationships and communications. Even the most horrendous or frightening face in a photograph may at least alert the patient to people they are likely to meet, and make such encounters less daunting!

Customer relations must be regarded as an ever developing dimension. There will always be room for improvement. Consumer feedback, staff initiatives and a groundwork of good training programmes are essential to the development of good customer relations.

One word of caution. Staff must never step over the line which separates common courtesy from familiarity. Patients and relatives are people and there are many, particularly in the older age-brackets, who object most strongly to being addressed by their first name. In their eagerness to put the patient at ease, staff may fall into the trap of calling an elderly person by a first name. This slip can have quite the opposite effect and damage the relationship.

On the other hand, there are many patients who would prefer to be on first name terms with the staff. It may be difficult for staff to know when to break with formalities and use first names. In practice, the patients themselves often ask staff what their full name is and then go on to ask whether they can use first names. Similarly, if patients feel staff are being too formal, they will probably say so. It is less likely that they will feel happy about speaking up in hostile circumstances. The important thing to recognise is that staff must be sensitive to the signals that patients are giving them. Each patient is different and has different preferences.

Customer relations is a very complex subject, involving sensitivity and responsiveness to individual needs, and its understanding and teaching must never be underplayed. Organisations can only be demonstrably successful if they have good relations with their customers, whoever they may be. Poor customer relations will spell disaster for any organisation in time. Forward trends are hard to reverse and detailed attention to promoting good relations is recommended as a fundamental requirement of any quality assurance programme.

"We are feeling quite well, thank you, sonny, and it's MRS
FOTHERINGTON-SMYTHE to you!!!"

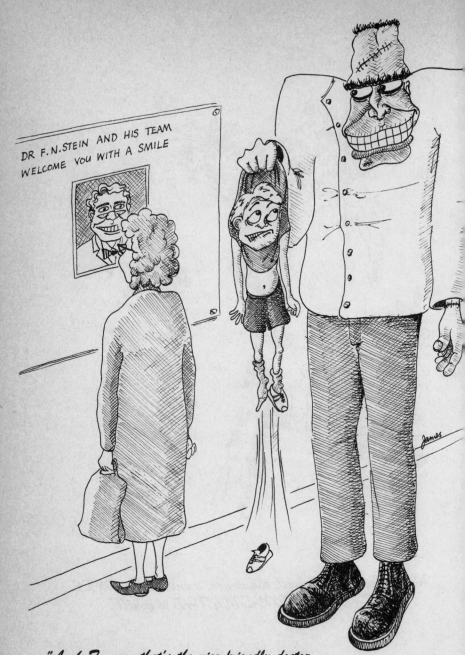

"Look Tommy, that's the nice friendly doctor
who will be looking after you"

Note

There are several words used to describe the recipient of NHS services—user, consumer, customer, patient—all have different connotations and much academic debate has revolved around the most suitable terms for the NHS setting. In looking at customer relations, we consider the 'customer' to be anyone who uses, or has contact with, any services wherever they are provided. This will include not only people receiving health care and their relatives, carers, and friends, but also members of the community in general as well as the NHS's own staff.

4 Patient satisfaction—what people think of us

While there are some ways of behaving that we may assume acceptable to most people, any attempt to establish and maintain good relations with our patients and clients must grapple with the knotty problem of what people actually want. In a world where our services must of necessity be rationed, we have to try to find out what kinds of services people would like before we can go on to refine, and make more acceptable, the way that those services are made available.

There are two pitfalls, more akin to chasms, in finding out what people want: firstly, have we given people sufficient information about services to enable them to make choices which have meaning for them; secondly, are we raising unrealistic expectations of what people may be able to get from us? To some extent, unrealistic expectations may have to be accepted as part of a dialogue with customers; in practice we have found that health professionals hold the key role in assessing what information the patient or client needs and in communicating the scope of services available. Attempts in our Unit to measure patient satisfaction have been made with these provisos in mind.

Apart from the issue of whether people have the information they need to answer our questions, certain client groups are not equipped to respond. Very frail or elderly people and those with learning difficulties are key users of our services and are especially vulnerable. Traditional methods of measuring patient satisfaction, such as questionnaires, are unsuitable. Clients may be unable to understand and/or respond to questions or, even worse, may feel obliged to give the 'right' answers, either for fear of recriminations or out of a sense of gratitude. The attitude of elderly people, in particular, to doctors and nurses tends to be unquestioning. The way through this maze must be led by the staff themselves, and managers must be aware of the qualities staff need to make themselves accessible to patients. We have found that different situations demand different qualities. The initiatives described in the rest of this chapter have therefore been underpinned by two principles:

- the staff involved must understand the purpose of the exercise and what it can achieve for patients and
- the method used must be chosen with the needs of the client group concerned in mind

Exploit your resources!

In setting up the patient satisfaction quality group, we felt it was important to recognise that a lot of valuable and relevant work had already been done and was, in many cases, still ongoing. This is as true for the monitoring of patient satisfaction as it is for many other areas now claimed as the remit of the quality lobby. Although some of this work was in the shape of formal surveys, other methods of working have developed which can yield useful information as a by-product of routine work in the health service: the trusting relationships which exist between patients or clients and certain types of staff, and the mechanisms for dealing with complaints and compliments are examples.

The patient satisfaction group established that its overall purpose is: to encourage or initiate the measurement of patient satisfaction; to establish mechanisms for promoting and improving it; and to apply measures to assess the effect of those mechanisms. More specifically, the group had a responsibility:

- to agree the areas of satisfaction which can be monitored
- to identify current and recent local initiatives to monitor or survey patient satisfaction
- to suggest areas for monitoring, taking account of the service objectives of the Unit
- to agree a priority list for these surveys and specify a timescale
- to provide guidance on survey methods and other measures and to provide facilities for analysis of results
- to receive reports from surveys
- to agree a plan for implementation of recommendations and appropriate monitoring methods in consultation with managers
- to advise the Unit Management Board of progress

Survey methods

There were four early steps to take in focusing on such methods of monitoring patient satisfaction:

1. Compiling a literature review on the subject for use by groups and staff.
2. Ensuring that at least one member of the group had some current and practical guidelines to share with staff. This was achieved through attendance at the King's Fund seminar on customer satisfaction.
3. Gathering information on work already done and under way across the Unit.
4. Establishing a mechanism for recording, advising on and monitoring future surveys.

This fourth step was achieved by circulating to heads of department a form for registration of projects, with a covering letter explaining the purposes of the register, which are:

- to ensure that the aim of each project is consistent with the aims of the Unit, and that results obtained can be acted on
- to avoid duplication of effort by creating a register of work
- to ensure appropriate ethical approval is sought
- to ensure the terms of the Data Protection Act 1974 are satisfied
- to encourage dissemination of ideas and experience
- to encourage awareness of the resource implications of survey work and design

The registration form was accompanied by advice on completion of a protocol from the Medical School's Department of Clinical Epidemiology.

Although it would be less than factual to claim 100 per cent response to this initiative, it did serve to emphasise the important legal and ethical considerations of some survey work, and to ensure that staff who needed advice or support knew where to find it.

Perhaps the most important consideration before starting any survey is to be clear about the aim of the project. It may sound obvious but many questionnaires are drawn up and used (or should we say 'inflicted') on service users, with scant regard to what the questioner actually wants to find out and intends, or is able, to do with the information the surveys elicit.

Careful thought and a realistic approach to likely results has often led us, at this point, to abandon formal questionnaire-based surveys in favour of other methods, where some of our client groups are concerned. As the usefulness, limitations and methodology of survey work is covered comprehensively elsewhere (see Bibliography), it is logical to move on to the area where managers and staff can use their skills more creatively—or maybe simply recognise and exploit the fact that they are already doing so!

Quality in Action . . . some practical steps

Patient surveys - notification of project

Title of project_____

Contact name_____

Post held_____

Contact name_____

Contact telephone number_____

Brief description of
project including aims_____

_____

_____

Is a protocol available?_____

Have you obtained ethical approval?_____

If using a computer, is the system
registered under the terms of the
Data Protection Act?_____

Proposed start date_____

Proposed end date of project_____

What will be the costs of
the proposed project?_____

Have the funds been identified?_____

If yes to the above, where from?_____

Quality in action . . . some practical steps

Patient surveys—results notification

Title of
project_____

Contact name_____

Aim of survey_____

Survey completed (date)_____

Summary of findings_____

_____

_____

Recommendations * _____

_____

_____

Date for review of action
follow-up survey_____

*
 Please attach report if appropriate

Note: This form may also be used to record results of follow-up
      surveys or projects

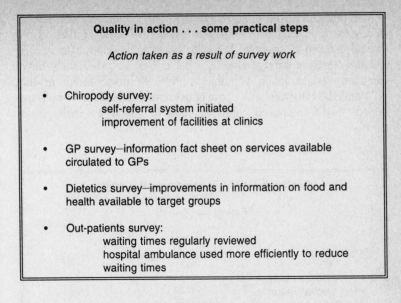

Quality in action . . . some practical steps

Action taken as a result of survey work

- Chiropody survey:
    self-referral system initiated
    improvement of facilities at clinics

- GP survey—information fact sheet on services available
  circulated to GPs

- Dietetics survey—improvements in information on food and
  health available to target groups

- Out-patients survey:
    waiting times regularly reviewed
    hospital ambulance used more efficiently to reduce
    waiting times

Non-survey methods—the patients talk back!

The special circumstances of elderly people in hospital may make
traditional methods of measuring patient satisfaction inappropriate.
Many may not be able to respond to questionnaires or may feel
obligated to express satisfaction. People in their seventies and eighties
today come from a generation taught to revere doctors as superior
beings and nurses as angels of mercy. Although these views are now
being inexorably eroded, they are much more common among the
elderly. This cultural attitude and the fact that many elderly patients
are confused and may be prone to feelings of persecution while in
hospital, demand an alternative method of finding out what the users
think.

Inspired by examples discussed at the King's Fund, the group
suggested setting up a patient user group at the hospital. The matron
of the hospital, a member of the group, wisely delegated this to the
Activities nurse. The significant point here is that this nurse does not
wear uniform and is in regular contact with patients through the social
activities arranged in the hospital, notably the evening social club. The
connection between the user group and the 'official' side of hospital
life was thus broken.

The minutes of the group's meetings are channelled back to the patient satisfaction group, mainly as a means of ensuring that action has been taken if possible. It has to be said, however, that this is usually merely a safety-valve . . . the nurses, or other staff, have frequently taken action as soon as they are made aware of the problems. It really has been a case of overlooking the obvious because nobody had complained before—a point to which we shall return shortly.

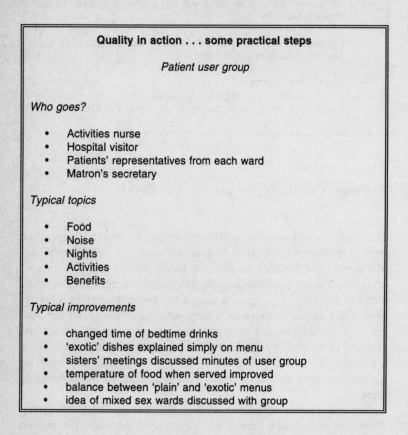

Quality in action . . . some practical steps

Patient user group

Who goes?

- Activities nurse
- Hospital visitor
- Patients' representatives from each ward
- Matron's secretary

Typical topics

- Food
- Noise
- Nights
- Activities
- Benefits

Typical improvements

- changed time of bedtime drinks
- 'exotic' dishes explained simply on menu
- sisters' meetings discussed minutes of user group
- temperature of food when served improved
- balance between 'plain' and 'exotic' menus
- idea of mixed sex wards discussed with group

Certain topics for the talkback user group, such as food and noise, have become regular features as the patients change. After the initial flurry of improvements (see panel) prompted by the discussions of the group, items which can be acted on have become less numerous but the group continues to fulfil two important functions in improving the quality of care; firstly, it identifies areas which matter to people in the hospital and provides the impetus to rectify problems where possible; secondly, it offers another social outlet to in-patients, one of whose main problems is coping with the boredom of a hospital stay.

What complaints tell us

A systematic approach to making quality a reality in the new NHS is to overlay a strategy for assuring quality on the business planning process. One of the key goals in any business must be to meet the needs of the client. How do we measure whether we are doing this? Before throwing ourselves headlong into an expensive routine of customer surveys, there is much to be said for looking at the existing complaints machinery. It may be able to do half of the job for us, while also helping to achieve another business goal—retaining a satisfied workforce. Because complaints are called complaints we tend to view them negatively and build in systems to deal with these nasty things as quickly as possible. We may not look at positive comments or compliments in an analytical way, possibly because the number of thank-you letters received on a ward usually outnumber complaints.

Although we do need to have an efficient system for processing them it is not enough to deal with complaints speedily and relax into complacency because that is to overlook an important resource. We should also look at what they can tell us about what we do well, what we can do better, and which of our staff and client groups need additional support or resources.

The limitations of patient questionnaires for some client groups have already been mentioned. Our approach was to set up a complaints monitoring group to look at three main issues:

- The quality of the procedures for handling complaints.
- The pattern of comments and complaints we receive.
- The action to be taken to prevent recurrence.

This approach reflects the familiar 'quality cycle'. Any quality initiative which has any chance of working in the real world has to have top level commitment. Our group consequently involved senior personnel, largely clinicians and managers, from each care group. We established with relative ease a list of good-practice guidelines on the maximum period for acknowledging letters, investigation and response; the reporting structure and follow up. These can be incorporated into contract agreements as a measure of response to consumers.

"A complaint! my God, we've had a complaint! – someone's head will roll for this!"

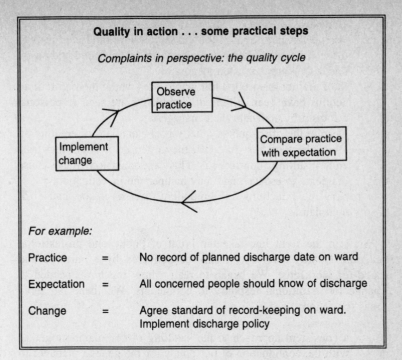

Quality in action . . . some practical steps

Complaints in perspective: the quality cycle

For example:

Practice   =   No record of planned discharge date on ward

Expectation   =   All concerned people should know of discharge

Change   =   Agree standard of record-keeping on ward.
                             Implement discharge policy

Quality in action . . . some practical steps

Monitoring complaints and good practice guidelines

- Acknowledgement of letter within one week

- Establish reason for, and category of, complaint

- Check tone, style and spelling of reply

- Send reply within six weeks

- Good record-keeping

- Support staff

We also identified the pattern of types of complaint. Some interesting points arose from our initial meetings:

- The reason for complaints is often not the actual incident focused on. Psychological and emotional causes are often evident.

- Positive remarks about staff and services are rarely fed back to those concerned. Again complaints are to be feared and swept under the carpet as soon as possible.
- Staff are not counselled following cases where their attitude or actions have been criticised. Complaints are seen as personal criticism by staff and their managers.
- Despite the often-quoted quality goal-statement of creating an atmosphere of trust for staff, they often do not feel that trust and resulting confidence. This apprehension may cause incidents to escalate and may hamper the investigation.
- Service reductions or limitations are a major cause of complaint.

Staff in the front line take the brunt of public and professional reaction. Quality service can only be delivered by a nurtured and cared-for workforce. We began to realise how much we needed to change the traditional response to complaints. We identified three areas for action:

- a consistent approach to the handling of complaints, together with the continuation of our policy for the general manager to meet with complainants if they so wish
- a reporting structure to the Unit Management Board which incorporates the pattern of complaints and follow up action
- a training programme, in partnership with our Personnel Department, on customer relations and counselling for managers on the needs of their front-line staff

This type of approach uses existing mechanisms to begin to address several of the issues surrounding the provision of quality health care for our clients:

- identifying and undertaking problems in current service provision
- supporting and feeding back to our main resource for quality—our staff—and supporting our contract tenders with factual evidence of our clients' response to us, both critical and complimentary, and of our response to them

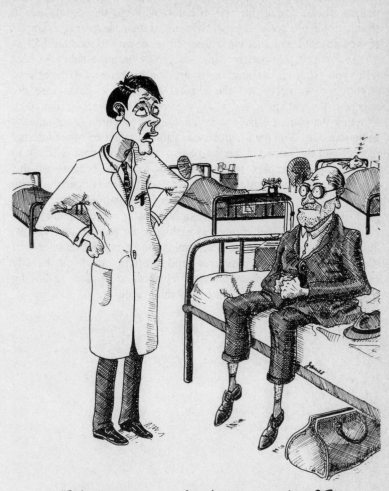

"What do you mean you haven't got any complaints? How are we supposed to run a service if you don't complain?"

What's in a name?

The problem with using 'satisfaction' in the names of quality groups or initiatives is that it implies that all we have to do is to see if the patient, client, or staff member is happy with our services or not. In truth, people are not always so clear-cut in their views. For example, if they do not know that the waiting times down the road are half as long as in your out-patient clinic, they may be quite happy to wait with you. If your waiting times are longer because GPs believe (rightly or wrongly) that the clinical standards of your care are superior, the patient is not always going to be aware of that fact. Whether the patient is truly satisfied with the situation is not an easy thing to judge. With the implications of the introduction of the internal market and the impact it has on patient choice, this area is likely to become more complex rather than less so. It is because of this complexity that the monitoring of patient satisfaction—or perhaps more accurately, attitudes—should be considered as a journey rather than a goal. It is vital to be aware of the limitations of survey methods and of the information and choices available to our patients and clients. Armed with this awareness, a determination to exploit the talents of the staff, and other initiatives and working methods already established, there are many practical advances to be made in finding out what people want and doing something about it.

"Now MR SIMPKINS is there anything you'd like to say about the quality of nursing care?"

5 Staff satisfaction and development—looking after ourselves

Progress in all the areas we cover in this book is dependent on the attitude of the staff and, therefore, the importance that management places on supporting and developing its workforce.

Staff are the most valuable resource in the health services. In all efficient organisations each member makes an essential contribution to the overall aim of the team. Yet in a health service which has set many cost improvement programmes, made efficiency savings, drafted hundreds of job descriptions, evaluated and graded posts under a number of schemes, the staff viewpoint has been largely ignored and a number feel their contribution is undervalued. Their opinion is rarely sought and as a result they are generally demoralised. Successful recruitment and retention of staff has proved to be difficult. There will be periods of high unemployment when there are considerable numbers of applicants for posts, which lead some managers into a false sense of security and complacency. They believe it is easy to recruit and that it does not matter if staff become disenchanted and leave because they are not difficult to replace. Those managers have failed to acknowledge the fact that the majority of people working in the National Health Service are highly committed individuals who have a wealth of experience and have shown extreme loyalty. To continue to demoralise these staff will do irreparable harm to the backbone of the service. It may not be easy to replace leavers with the same calibre of staff and therefore quality standards are likely to tumble. If the quantity of service offered can be equated with the size of the establishment, the quality can be related to the type of people who make up that establishment, the 'human' part of resources.

Knowing that, we should offer all levels of staff a good working environment and the best possible opportunity for development. The key role of the manager is to provide that opportunity and environment and then to measure the level of staff satisfaction. The main methods of assessing staff satisfaction will be recruitment and retention levels and sickness rates as successful retention and low sickness rates are directly related to staff satisfaction and high morale. These depend on five main elements:

1. Ensuring that all staff have jobs which are worthwhile and satisfying.
2. An acknowledgement and appreciation of each member of staff's personal contribution to the operation.
3. An adequate remuneration and reward system for the job.
4. An opportunity for professional and personal development.
5. Good buildings and facilities with a pleasant, welcoming environment and ambience.

It may be helpful to look at each of these in turn.

Ensuring that all staff have jobs which are worthwhile and satisfying—reprofiling the workforce

Managers have a responsibility to ensure that the total job content for each member of staff is worthwhile and satisfying. The job descriptions which are issued to staff on appointment are often too long, badly constructed, and over complicated. They are seldom subject to review and, if this was undertaken, it would often be found that at least one element of the original job description was now quite irrelevant, having its origin in the past and now having no effect on the achievement of organisational goals.

Each post should be thoroughly analysed and reviewed regularly with the post-holder to ensure that obsolete tasks are substituted by something which is meaningful and helps the rest of the organisation. At the same time, the opportunity should be taken to ensure that the skills of staff are matched to the required tasks. The techniques of job design, job analysis and reprofiling the workforce are well described elsewhere (see Bibliography). A review of job content is particularly important at times of stress. Management's recognition of the increased pressure on individuals and the adjustment of workload and focus will help to motivate staff. It is important that those, often the personnel officers, who have responsibility for constructing job descriptions, understand and appreciate the goals of the organisation and department. Job descriptions should focus on those goals instead of the usually long all-embracing 'mustn't leave anything out' lists of responsibilities which are handed out to staff.

43

Examples of outdated job descriptions are not difficult to find in any organisation. For example, a member of staff may have been given the task of filing away items neatly in chronological order, but these items may be neither asked for nor looked at, ever again. Such a task must be totally dissatisfying for the individual and an expensive waste of resources in terms of manpower, time, and space to the organisation. Elimination of the task would not only benefit the organisation financially but giving a more worthwhile task to the jobholder would result in greater job satisfaction. All reporting documentation, which can be tedious to complete, should be reviewed to ensure that tedium is reduced to a minimum. Once this exercise has been completed and improved procedures implemented, staff morale will improve. Staff should be encouraged to put forward their ideas and allowed to express creativity and initiative. When undertaking quality reviews of aspects of their own jobs they will be able to highlight changes which will result in improved efficiency or effectiveness, and these changes can then be incorporated in the job description. Reviews of nursing and domestic service procedures may well suggest a shift of some responsibility to the other's job description, which can lead to better patient care and, sometimes, to an improvement in team-work.

An acknowledgement and appreciation of each member of staff's personal contribution to the organisation

We often hear members of staff say that they do not see their manager or claim that he or she may not know what that particular member of staff actually does. Managers cannot afford to remain deskbound and should make themselves readily available to staff. Management must be seen making regular visits around the organisation to see staff and facilities. People should feel that they are noticed and that they matter. During these walkabouts, the manager can talk to individuals and show a personal understanding and appreciation of their contribution. Such approval is totally different from the practice of criticism and blame which has become all too common in the health service.

The successful manager will be the one who makes the effort to get to know the staff, enquires after their health and welfare, remembers details of, and asks about, their family, hobbies, and so on. Successful managers will always praise staff for their effort and contribution before suggesting a change. The reason for change should always be explained and discussed with the member of staff involved before directing implementation. Such an approach will ensure a motivated,

The open door policy!

energetic and responsive workforce.

Praising the domestic staff on the cleanliness of a corridor, the gardeners on the appearance of the lawns and flower beds, the painters on the decor, and the catering staff on the quality of the food, will ensure that when improvements are necessary, the staff feel less threatened by criticism. For example, the introduction of primary nursing in one of the geriatric wards led to some rivalry and we noticed the patients describing a particular nurse as 'theirs'. We, and the relatives, found this positive and reassuring. Often this approach may create an atmosphere of friendly rivalry or competition between departments. The successful manager can allow this to develop to a degree as it will help to motivate staff, but the competitiveness may become so great as to fragment the organisation so that it fails in its overall aim.

It is important that managers learn to differentiate between the contribution made by different groups of staff. Some jobs are necessarily more skilful and demand a higher level of training, but that does not mean that that particular post is more valuable to the organisation than a less skilful one. Each is vital to the success and smooth-running of the hospital. An absent porter can upset the balance of efficiency just as much as the absence of, say, an occupational therapist. Every post has its own skills and special importance in the hospital. Teamwork training has to recognise this and build on it.

An adequate remuneration and reward system

National Health Service salaries have been tied to national norms set by the review bodies, such as the Whitley Council, since the introduction of the service. The National Health Service reforms have opened the way for flexible pay negotiations, and those managers who can successfully pick their way through the minefield of flexible pay arrangements may reap the rewards of a free-hand in the recruitment and retention of staff.

It is not the purpose of this book to discuss the advantages or disadvantages of such arrangements other than to comment that increases in salaries in a competitive market are often paid for by decreasing the number of staff employed, unless of course the organisation can achieve a monopoly position and so increase its prices. A monopoly position does not predominate in the health-care market. There is also a danger that if salaries are not fairly and equally adjusted across the board then certain groups of staff will be disadvantaged and feel undervalued.

At the present time, there may be some dissatisfaction that salary rates within the National Health Services are lower than in local government and the private sector, but this can be compensated for by job satisfaction and security. Staff seldom leave solely because of this salary differential. The reason for disenchantment is generally a combination of factors which includes a lack of recognition in the organisation, poor communications and so on. It is the responsibility of managers to ensure that the contribution of staff is not undervalued and that some recognition is given for years of service and endeavour.

In our Unit, long and loyal service has been rewarded with a dinner to which husbands, wives and partners are invited and the long servers are presented with a small certificate which acknowledges their service.

The opportunity is also taken on such occasions to present achievement awards to anyone who has made some outstanding contribution during the year. For example, a health visitor who has, in addition to carrying out his or her main responsibilities, produced a profile of available services which can be given to families. Sisters and nursing staff have been given buckles depicting the hospital crest for achieving certain set lengths of service. There are many ingenious ways of rewarding staff for loyalty from paperweights to ties and brooches. It is not the value of the reward but the acknowledgement of value which is important and meaningful to staff.

Quality in action . . . some practical steps

Rewarding staff

- New uniforms

- Buckles, ties, etc.

- Long service awards

- Achievement awards

- Regular events:
  barbecues
  parties
  fêtes

- Retirement and leaving parties

- Passing on invitations, theatre tickets

To add to the sense of occasion, the chairman of the health authority, the chief executive, or a celebrity, can be invited to present the awards. The cost of such an event and the award is negligible when compared to the immense pleasure and satisfaction derived by the staff who receive their due recognition. These functions always seem to boost morale and help to promote the corporate spirit. Needless to say it is essential that the efforts of all members of staff are acknowledged at these events.

An opportunity for professional and personal development

Professional development for clinical staff has been a subject for debate and review by universities, colleges, schools and authorities for

---

Quality in action . . . some practical steps

Training

Outside

- Approved courses

- Conferences

- Visits to other centres

In-house

- Quality circles

- Multidisciplinary team meetings

- Case conferences

- Mandatory training:
  Security
  Fire
  Health and safety
  Avoid violence
  Self-defence
  Drugs
  Lifting and back care
  Control of infection
  Injections

---

a number of years, and it is not intended to detail it within these pages. Nevertheless it must be recognised that the mere attainment of a professional qualification does not allow the professional to forsake the classroom, the lecture theatre, the textbooks or the journals. All professional staff should be given the opportunity, and helped, to keep up to date. Time should be allowed for attendance at meetings, case conferences, and quality groups including clinical audit. We have developed mandatory training programmes for nurses and health visitors covering subjects such as drugs, giving injections, infection control, lifting programmes, which have been welcomed and helped staff to keep up to date. We are confident that these courses will be of value in promoting quality. In time we will need to audit these training programmes to ensure that they have actually reduced untoward incidents. The remainder of this chapter is mainly devoted to non-clinical staff but the comments on personal development may well equally apply to clinical staff.

There are many staff who entered the National Health Service in their late teens or early twenties and who settled into administrative and other posts which suited their abilities at that time. Many of these people have stayed in these posts for the remainder of their careers. Some managers may have bothered to meet individual members of staff to discuss their career aspirations or a change in post to continue personal development. It must be recognised that a small number of people may wish to remain in the same post, but there are a greater number who would like to move to a more responsible post as they develop. The National Health Service has traditionally paid scant attention to the professional and personal development of the lower-paid and lower-graded non-clinical staff—the administrative and clerical grades, for example. On joining the Unit, the General Manager found to his dismay that there were a number of staff who were frustrated because they had been given no opportunity for development, nor had they received promotions in up to thirty-five years of service. An immediate response could be that this was because they did not merit it. But it was found that when these staff were given an opportunity, many had skills and potential which had never been fully realised or appreciated. It was possible to develop some of this potential at a late stage, but it was sad to reflect on what might have been if only they had been given an earlier opportunity.

Each member of staff should be seen regularly by their manager to discuss their personal development and career aspirations. Professional and personal development can then be encouraged and achieved by changes in job content and increased responsibility. In our view, although some of the increasing numbers of courses which are available may be helpful, much professional and personal development for staff can be carried out more effectively in house. There is a need to develop rotational training and exchange posts for the lower and middle grades of staff, and more multidisciplinary in-house training schemes should be established.

Personal development is as important as professional development and people now have higher expectations of their jobs. Within our Unit a number of staff are now doing totally different jobs from those that they were doing five years ago. There are of, course, a number of staff who have chosen to remain in their established posts, but every encouragement has been given to staff to develop. A number of staff have enlisted in commercial courses, such as counselling and business management, which are not readily available locally. These new-found skills have then been used both professionally and to train other staff.

Some training might seem to be out of the ordinary but even some of the more obscure courses may help personal development and the organisation. The list is endless but, for example, certain senior managers' eyebrows were raised in response to requests from our Unit for the Endowments Fund to pay for driving lessons for a number of our peripatetic therapists. After some discussion the courses were eventually allowed and the district has been more than adequately rewarded by those staff who have now become a more mobile and responsive force. If the health authority demands that a post-holder must be able to drive a car to carry out his or her duties then it is difficult to see the argument that driving lessons are any different from a management course.

We also have a responsibility, as employers, for the welfare and safety of our staff. Wandsworth, an inner London area, may have a bigger problem than some other authorities, but awareness of violence and how to avoid and deal with it is another part of enabling our employees to feel comfortable and confident at work. Mandatory training in how to avoid violence and how to protect oneself is necessary for certain at-risk staff, but all staff should be encouraged to take part in this training. Similarly, all staff should be encouraged to undergo regular training in fire prevention and protection and other aspects of health and safety at work. All of this training should be regarded as part of professional and personal development.

Good facilities and a pleasant environment to work in

The value of a comfortable environment for staff satisfaction is discussed in Chapter 6. A number of staff will be required to be resident as part of their duties and others will want residential accommodation for convenience. Personnel managers have always stressed the importance of residential accommodation in recruitment programmes, yet we have allowed our residences to deteriorate over the years. This dilapidation has caused discontent among staff, and bodies such as the Royal Colleges of Surgeons and Physicians have threatened to withdraw recognition from certain hospitals on account of the habitability of doctors' residences. The rent derived from residential accommodation has often been used to bolster other services and has not been ploughed back into maintenance of the estate, so one of the largest capital assets of the health service has now become an even larger liability, especially in view of the proposed capital charging arrangements. Proper attention must be paid to the improvement of all accommodation in the health service. A good standard of accommodation will benefit the staff who, in turn, will benefit the organisation.

Staff satisfaction can be measured in a number of ways, such as successful recruitment and retention figures, low sickness level reviews, interest in extra-curricular activities like fun runs and charity fêtes, but it is important that a leaving questionnaire and interview is held with each employee at the time of termination of contract. These can reveal a number of areas of possible discontent and allow changes to be made before the situation gets totally out of hand. Staff who return to work at a hospital they previously left also provide a useful measure. Five years ago many of our student nurses had declared that they never wished to see our hospital again. It is gratifying, now, to find that over twenty recently qualified nurses asked to return to us to undertake their staff nursing. A good indicator that things have begun to improve!

But we should not be complacent. Williams, Soothill and Barry found in a study which followed up nurses who had left an organisation, that 40 per cent left to continue nursing elsewhere in the organisation, 26 per cent went into the private sector and 23 per cent left to have a family. Only 11 per cent actually left nursing for good. It is therefore crucial that we find ways of encouraging some of those 49 per cent who left to have families, or left the service to take up posts in the private sector, to return to the National Health Service. There is a need to provide creche facilities and to continue to be innovative by introducing part-time working and job-sharing schemes and remembering that part-timers require the same job security and privileges as full-time staff. Staff are invaluable to the success of any organisation—ignore them at your peril, invest in them and you will be rewarded.

6 Physical environment—creating the right atmosphere

The majority of hospitals which are presently in use in the United Kingdom were built just before, or at the turn of, the twentieth century. Although our Victorian and Edwardian forbears were excellent architects and craftsmen, their hospitals were built for styles of practice and treatment which have long since been outmoded by the rapid developments in medicine and surgery. The hurried upgradings and alterations to accommodate changing practice have often been ill-conceived, and their execution has sadly failed to match up to the high standards and elegance of the original buildings. Cost-cutting has necessarily led to inferior workmanship, and patient and staff amenities have often been sacrificed in order to contain costs. Cramped and insufficient waiting areas in out-patients departments, the loss of privacy in wards due to poor design, ineffective and insufficient screening, poor and inadequate changing facilities for staff, and too few toilets, are all common examples of how the desire to save money has led to a reduction in the quality of services.

At the same time, the cost of developments in treatment and the increase in demand for health services has been paid for at the expense of routine and essential maintenance to the fabric of the hospital. Additional factors have compounded the problem; competitive tendering for cleaning services has frequently resulted in a fall in standards of cleanliness and comfort in the hospital environment. Consequently, as British hospitals now reach and pass their centenaries, they are showing the signs of years of neglect. Managers accept dingy and dirty corridors as commonplace and a fact of life in the National Health Service.

Scandals in mental illness institutions continue to make the headlines. Food poisoning has occurred in hospitals for the elderly due to the lack of adequate hygiene and facilities in kitchens. Previously painted surfaces become discoloured, chipped and covered in frayed, tattered, out-of-date notices or graffiti. Signposting, if existent, is sometimes misleading. Garden areas are overgrown and hospital grounds are allowed to become littered with rubbish and debris.

Car parking, or rather the lack of it, on many hospital sites is a contentious issue which upsets patients, visitors and staff alike, yet there are many senior managers who pronounce that they want nothing to do with the problem. Responsibility for site services is not always viewed as the concern of senior management. Such attitudes, if allowed to continue, will have a serious deleterious effect on the hospital's ability to attract business in the health care market. Ease of access to parking is identified as the chief reason for the success of Tesco's revival in the 1980s as a major force in the retail food industry. While hospitals are not dealing with the same business as the supermarket giants, access is a cornerstone of quality for any service industry. Car parking difficulties invariably anger staff and lead to discontent and loss of morale. The senior manager who evades this issue will only have himself or herself to blame when low morale affects the recruitment and retention of staff. It would be easy to continue to list many other examples of neglect in the fabric of our health care sites. All of these have a profound effect on the attitudes of patients, relatives and staff.

Undoubtedly, the lack of maintenance and cleanliness breeds a behavioural pattern which is self perpetuating. If people see a littered corridor then who can blame them if they do not place their rubbish in a litter-bin but merely drop it on the floor. One more item of rubbish is probably unlikely to make much difference to the general untidiness. Managers have often turned a blind eye to this sorry state and can walk along corridors without noticing litter and filth. This neglect, however, leads to further untidiness, damage and vandalism. The senior manager who sets an example by picking up rubbish and placing it in a bin is an exception.

The cleanliness of the hospital depends on teamwork. Everyone, from the most senior manager to the most junior member of staff, has a responsibility for cleanliness. All members of staff must develop a responsible attitude, and if rubbish is seen in a corridor staff should pick it up and place it in a bin. Once this is accepted by one group it quickly spreads to others. The psychological effect of seeing someone pick up a piece of rubbish eventually deters litterers. Collective responsibility is also essential in clinical areas, and we have found that nurses and domestics have developed a team approach in dealing with clinical spillages and accidents.

Run down and dilapidated surroundings are unpleasant for the users, giving an immediate impression of poor service, and indeed it is likely that the actual service delivered will be inferior. Staff morale is adversely affected if people are forced to work in a run-down and uncared for environment. A successful recruitment and staff retention programme is highly dependent on an attractive and pleasant environment. Both patient and staff satisfaction questionnaires reveal the importance of the hospital and clinic environment. It is imperative, therefore, for managers to give immediate attention to all areas of the hospital environment, and to ensure that it is maintained to the highest standards at all times. Failure in this objective in the future will have dire consequences. The reasons are not only identifiable in qualitative items but the effects of capital charging and of the removal of crown immunity will force us to pay attention even if we will not do so for the sake of patients and staff.

It is important that we appreciate that every patient is a person and each is a 'paying' patient. The source of payment may differ but each will be looking for the best service and the best value for money. Services will be judged as much on the non-clinical as on the clinical standard, and our ability to survive in this competitive market will, therefore, also depend on the standards of the non-clinical services such as the environment. Clinical services will undoubtedly benefit from improvements in equipment, buildings and ambience.

There are many of us who are all too familiar with the extra care and attention which is given to public areas at the time of visits by dignitaries, yet such areas as public cloakrooms, rest rooms, and changing rooms not included in the dignitaries' itinerary can be left in a squalid state. The boost to morale anticipated from the visit of the VIP is nullified by the cynicism expressed by staff at the double standard. There is a responsibility to ensure that all areas of health care premises are continually maintained to a high standard at all times. Every day should be regarded as a red-letter day and not just those when a dignitary is expected, for, after all, every patient and every member of staff is a special person.

"The Princess is coming!"

The cost of backlog maintenance will now be extremely high in the more neglected areas in the health service, but we cannot afford not to remedy the defects and improve the estate. To continue to procrastinate will not only increase capital charges but will affect our ability to attract patients and staff and will make us less competitive in the market place. Once the basic work has been carried out, regular audits of buildings, facilities, equipment and the environment should be conducted, and will form part of the total quality assurance programme. Ideally, this audit should be carried out by a multidisciplinary team, including a good representation of all users of the service. The needs of individuals and groups will be different, but all of these must be taken into account when auditing and in design and development programmes. The results of the audit will be used to determine priorities and to help develop programmes to convert hospitals and health-care premises into high quality facilities which are attractive to both patients and staff. As a cautionary note, it is important to ensure that, as cost improvement programmes become more difficult to identify, the follies of the past are not repeated by reducing maintenance. Adequate sums of money must be made available to maintain the estate. In the same way that companies cannot afford not to advertise, hospitals cannot afford not to maintain a high quality image.

There are innumerable exciting and innovative ways of making the hospital environment more user-friendly, welcoming, and homely, overcoming the traditional alternatives of drab dinginess or daunting clinical starkness.

Hospitals should be proud to display their names and emblems on outside walls. The hospital flag will instil a sense of pride of belonging in the staff. Entrances should be clearly indicated and ensure easy access for the elderly and disabled. Signposting within the hospital should be clear, accurate and easy to follow. Prohibiting notices should be kept to a minimum as they are not welcoming. Difficult routes can be indicated by the use of coloured stripes on walls, or decorative patterns or panels.

The monotony of the plastered walls in corridors, waiting areas, and some clinical areas can be broken by the use of anaglypta or woodchip wallpaper covered with a vinyl emulsion which is fairly easy to wash down. Interestingly, we have found that people tend to be more careful with a wallpaper surface and take infinite care to avoid damage. Our impression is that the wallpapered surfaces are lasting better than the uncovered plaster. The use of thirty-centimetre strips of varnished wood, fixed horizontally at about a metre off the ground, looks good and has the advantage of giving added protection

"How should I know what it says? It's all Greek to me!!"

to the walls from possible damage by wheelchairs and trolleys. Wall surfaces can be further improved by the use of pictures and photographs. Cheap pictures are easily obtained, but many calendars lend themselves to framing and make attractive, interesting, and lasting pictures. More expensive pictures can be borrowed quite cheaply from such organisations as Art in Hospitals. Pictures help to make the decor look more like home. Ringing the changes with new pictures will help to keep up the interest of staff in their place of work. Old posters also make excellent pictures and have the added advantage of stirring memories. We have found these very useful as a reminiscence exercise for elderly people.

Quality in action . . . some practical steps

Improving the environment

- Improve standards of cleanliness

- Improve standards of painting and decor

- Introduce pictures

- Use of carpets

- Use of wallpaper or other attractive wallcovering

- Flowers, window boxes, garden areas

- Furniture

- Fish tanks

- Statues, decorative glass panels, etc.

- Ornaments

- Menus

- Signposting

- Lighting

- Heating and ventilation

- Seating

- Rest rooms

It is also worth remembering that talent abounds among local artists, sculptors and craftsmen, who are eager for recognition. Their work can be commissioned at very reasonable rates. A sculpture in the out-patients department or in the grounds, stained glass or engraved glass panels, pottery, wicker stools, and toys for children all add interest and brighten the environment.

Quality in action . . . some practical steps

Creating an image

- Be proud of the history

- Display the hospital name

- Display the hospital emblem or flag

- Display 'Welcome' notices

- Identifiable uniforms for all staff

- Name badges with hospital logo

- Improve standards of cleanliness

- Improve standards of maintenance

- Personal and individualised service

- Photographs of all key personnel displayed in appropriate public areas

- Open days

- Formal invitations to well-known personalities to visit or open refurbished areas

- Public relations:

    articles in local newspapers
    speaking to local groups

Fish tanks with brightly coloured fish will relieve the boredom of waiting areas. The addition of real flowers and plants in window boxes and planters improves the ambience and interest for patient, visitor and staff. Patients will occasionally volunteer to 'see to the flowers' and this can be encouraged as an activity exercise. Artificial plants are useful to brighten dark interior corners, the modern silk-type are far more lifelike and attractive than the perennial plastic which can be the bane of the hospital ward. The use of hanging baskets will brighten a dull exterior and, where it is difficult to create a natural garden, astra-turf and container plants can be used to good effect.

The financing of some of these suggested improvements may at first appear to be insurmountable, but we have found that talking to local organisations, public houses and schools has encouraged them to support a number of these projects keenly. For example, one of our local schools' art classes designed and made a superb stained-glass panel to replace a grey window at the entrance to the out-patients department. Local groups are often happy to be identified with their local hospital and are generous in their support. A public house which bears the same name as the hospital puts aside one evening occasionally when patients are invited as guests and all proceeds from sales to other customers are generously donated to the hospital.

To digress slightly, other local organisations will give time to sit with those patients who have no visitors or accompany others on shopping expeditions or trips to museums, gardens and theatres. Some local residents who have good-natured, trusted, docile and house-trained dogs can be encouraged to visit the hospital on a regular basis to brighten the long hours of a patient's day. A few of our visiting dogs happily leave their owners at the hospital entrance and make their way to their allocated wards to meet their adopted friends. The idea of allowing animals onto any hospital ward would have been unthinkable a few years ago; this initiative highlights the importance of challenging the traditional values and routines of the hospital environment.

Further ideas can be pooled, and support enlisted, to continue the improvement programme. We have been grateful to several relatives and staff who have donated pictures, furniture, a piano, and fish tanks. On a grander scale, the local authority, having seen the cleaned façade of the hospital building, generously financed the replacement of a damaged wall with railings which were in keeping with the style and period of the building. Perhaps there is an inherent desire to be associated with improvement or success, but support and help is always welcome and makes the task of improving the environment much easier.

Blueprints cannot be laid down as to how hospitals should improve their environment or image. Each hospital and health service site has its own unique characteristics. We have attempted to indicate a number of areas we targeted, but each health care unit must decide for itself its own improvement programme. There is a tremendous sense of satisfaction in implementing, and continuing to look, for further ways of improving the hospital environment. This satisfaction has been shared by the staff, all of whom are eager to be involved and now take great pride in the appearance and the ambience of their hospital.

7 Information—everybody's business

Although the availability of good quality information has always been important to good management in the health service, the advent of the new Health Service Act has made it a prerequisite. Timely, relevant and accurate data are now essential to the development, honouring and monitoring of contracts and hence to the survival of provider units. Just as good information is integral to the business of health care, so it is integral to the provision of quality in health care in all its manifestations. Contract management, clinical audit, and patient and staff satisfaction hinge on the availability and accessibility of good record and information systems and procedures, and must also be measured and evaluated by the intelligent use of data.

Information is too often seen in organisations as a mysterious and isolated 'bolt-on' function, particularly where many different disciplines of staff with their own well-established specialisms already exist. In order to move information and information technology away from this image and make it work for health providers, a people-oriented approach to the development and implementation of systems is needed. The success of this approach depends on how closely the operational needs of health professionals, and other 'coal-face' staff, and management match the objectives of the organisation. Because of the diversity of the types of staff working within the health service, making information meaningful and helpful is a hugely complex task. Although the deployment of technically flexible computer systems goes a long way to achieving this, it is far more important to get over to the staff providing the service the practicalities of introducing information systems and information use. If you get that right, the quality of data and therefore the quality of the service can benefit enormously.

Donabedian's method for appraising and evaluating quality can be a useful way of placing information in its proper place. Donabedian identifies three components of quality measurement:

Structure $\rightarrow$ Process $\rightarrow$ Outcome $\rightarrow$

Within an organisation we can look at this information thus:

Data $\rightarrow$ Information $\rightarrow$ Intelligence $\rightarrow$

where the processing of raw data, by computer or manually, sorts them into a recognisable and transferable format, and where this format (a table, a graph, or maybe a chart) is then used to draw some useful conclusion or premise (the intelligence, or outcome of the whole procedure).

Tools $\rightarrow$ Work $\rightarrow$ Results $\rightarrow$

Similarly, we can look at data as the tools we use to do work (the process) out of which we expect to see results (the outcome). This concept can help to emphasise that computer systems and all information processing are there to serve the ends of the organisation and its people, not the other way round! The objectives of resource management remain the key to the development of good information use in the National Health Service, but the emphasis on installing computer systems as an end in itself, rather than the means to an end, has given information technology a bad name among many health professionals.

Making decisions based on good quality information is not easy in an environment where information has traditionally been designed round a set of central requirements which are output-led, rather than outcome-led, in health terms. Although defining and measuring outcome is undoubtedly difficult, the concentration on activity from the centre has led to the introduction of computers which are not flexible enough to respond either to the changing management needs of the service or to the advances in thinking about what health care should really be about. As most people in the health service have had their first taste of computing in this setting, the reputation of information and information technology has suffered from the outset with the only people who can really make it work, the field staff.

As some type of statutory requirement to provide data centrally is likely to remain for all health care providers for the foreseeable future, and assuming that central requirements continue to be limited in their usefulness for local managerial and operational purposes, the need for flexible systems is paramount. The difficulty of developing systems which produce central requirements as a by-product has been well illustrated over the years since the implementation of the Korner Steering groups' recommendations. Hopefully, the recent advances in information technology will enable us to move away from systems whose structure is inflexible and centrally controlled, to smaller, powerful, local systems which can be interfaced with others to form comprehensive but responsive databases. This may mean we invest in more programming and design expertise in house, but it should also mean that the users can start tailoring their own systems to their own needs.

The singer not the song—lessons learned the hard way!

No matter how flexible and powerful information systems become, the quality of their end product depends on the people who capture, record, produce, analyse and interpret data.

Those working in the community have a better opportunity to get to grips with information than those in the hospital setting. As each nurse or practitioner must record their contacts with each individual patient or client, they are forced to confront the dilemma of using information: the more you want to get out of the system, the more you have to collect. Even with sophisticated data capture methods, this can mean more time spent on non-patient care. When a practitioner is the only person visiting someone at home, there will not be a clerk there to do the paperwork.

Introducing a regional computer system designed to collect community Korner data taught us many lessons about involving health professionals in the whole process. While we recognised that the peculiar characteristics of community nursing offered a unique opportunity to develop the system in harmony with the professionals' own needs and methods of working, we underestimated the constraints of the system, our own resources and the complexities and potential of the service the system was attempting to describe.

The most important thing when implementing a system is to get commitment to it. The commitment of staff managers does not necessarily guarantee the staff's own commitment, and inability to produce results for the effort put in is likely to result in the dissipation of whatever enthusiasm has been won at the start. During the first year of implementing the system we failed to deliver reliable or regular results back to the professionals and to the data entry clerks involved in recording data. We thus had problems with data-entry clerk retention and with professionals supporting the clerical staff. This made our resource problem worse and the quality of data going into the system suffered accordingly.

Our difficulties were not caused by inadequate resourcing alone, however, nor by the limitations of the computer's design. These are things which each organisation has to tackle within its own particular environment. The key issue, which we did not deal with properly, was how we involved the professionals. This has to do with setting the introduction of information technology within the goals and objectives of the organisation and is, therefore, relevant to the approach to quality which this book describes. We consulted representatives of all involved disciplines of staff from the different localities within our district. We did not disregard any suggestion on coding of community programmes and contacts. We acted on as many as possible, given the constraints of the computer programme, and changed codes frequently in the implementation period. Our belief was that the staff involved would appreciate our responsiveness and deferment to their professionalism, and that this would compensate for the inconsistency of data during the early stages of the exercise.

Of course, any health professional can tell you that there are as many different views on what a contact is, or how long it is before a 'hospital discharge' becomes a 'chronic client', as there are health professionals, and we finally had to lay down some rules for expediency's sake which pleased few as they felt no ownership of them. We had, in effect, lost the valuable consultation time which should have been spent in examining what the service offers and why.

Quality in action . . . some practical steps

Lessons learned in implementation

- Make sure purpose of system matches one or more of the organisation's objectives

- Publicise purpose of system to health professionals

- Don't put your faith in cascade training—train one to one wherever possible

- Overestimate data-entry time needed at the start

- Calculate required training time—double it

- Consult the health professionals early on and 'talent spot' for IT naturals

- Don't promise what you can't deliver!

This is where the quality assurance approach that the nurses have followed can be exploited. The principal functions of a group of staff are an ideal way of describing the key items that the information system should collect and produce. Unless the coding system design is underpinned by the objectives of the service, you will either have to be prescriptive about the design or allow for the chaos of open consultation. The first path will rob the staff of any sense of ownership, the second will exhaust you and corrupt the integrity of your information.

Breaking down the barriers

Removing the mystique of computers for many people is becoming more important than ever in the face of advances in the automation of systems and the need for good data in order to survive in the internal market.

The National Health Service Training Authority (now a directorate of the NHS Management Executive) recommended targeting training in the use of information and information technology at four groups[11]:

- IT specialists
- health care professionals
- clerical support staff
- health care managers

We decided that the best way to prepare for the structured approach to IT training which will be adopted across the district was to establish a general awareness-raising programme across the Unit. The objectives and structure of this programme allowed the computer-shy to raise their heads above the bunker without fear—a lot of other people did not understand the jargon either, they were just better at hiding the fact!

This programme was instituted in line with the terms of reference of the information quality group:

- identify the information that health service staff need to provide care for clients and patients
- involve staff in the use of information systems and give them access to the information they need
- make staff, patients and clients aware of the appropriate legislation covering access to personal information, and the importance of, and procedures for, maintaining confidentiality

in all areas where personal information is concerned
- ensure that any changes to information systems are compatible with the needs of the service—i.e. the ability to identify and cost services at the appropriate level
- simplify existing systems to enable the auditing of data quality and clinical content
- establish a meaningful link between the effects of finance, staffing and activity

---

Quality in action . . . some practical steps

Computer awareness

The aim: to make the best possible use of computing resources by promoting among all staff an awareness of the basics of computing and information systems.

Content of an awareness session:

- Overview

- Computer basics:
    Jargon
    What is 'hardware' and 'software'?
    On-line systems/stand-alone PCs

- Computers in action—demonstration of personal computing potential

- Computer systems in the organisation

- Security and legal aspects of computing

Initial items for discussion included:

- methods of improving the accuracy of data collection
- systems for monitoring data accuracy
- a 'minimum data set' of information to be made available to health professionals
- development of a confidentiality policy

Information and the patient's rights

The shift towards a patient-focused health service was mentioned in our chapter on clinical audit in the context of access to records. The other side of this coin is confidentiality. Both these issues have been addressed recently by statute. The Data Protection Act (1974) establishes laws for the protection of computerised personal information. The Access to Health Records Act (1990) extends the patient's access rights from computerised data only to all records. As mentioned above, understanding of confidentiality should be a part of a computer awareness programme for all staff, but the need to design or commission systems which are readily 'translatable' to the layperson should be considered by information managers and general managers at the outset.

Several specialties have already introduced patient-held records, notably obstetrics and paediatrics (parent-held!), and, with the advent of the Patient's Charter, we hope that many more will follow. The implications for clinicians may be more obvious at first than those for information managers and computing managers. Although the incidences of requests for access have not been great up until the present (April, 1992), our systems are not particularly patient friendly. This may be too much to ask of a system whose primary purpose is to support the treatment of patients, but we should be thinking now of the kind of data people will be asking for and the availability of printouts in concise and logical format.

Anticipation of information needs is essential to the development of a good-quality information service; the addition of the patient to the list of information users should not be so astounding!

Information and the reforms

There are many differences surrounding the information requirements of purchasers and providers; the former will be looking at health needs assessment and outcomes for their populations, the latter will be accounting for the costs of service delivery. Both will, however, be looking for the balance between what we put in and what we get out, in information and health terms. A workforce willing and able to supply and use the data they must, and can, collect will be an advantage to both protagonists in the changed NHS.

Although the NHSTA's target groups for training are entirely appropriate, there are advantages to be gained from involving everyone who is willing in the most basic training in IT. Knowledge of the functions of the average personal computer software package and the difference between a computer terminal and a stand-alone personal computer can be terrifically empowering and thus relevant to everyone.

To the three criteria for information which Edith Körner stipulated—timeliness, accuracy and relevance—should be added simplicity and clarity. Despite the mind-boggling power of modern technology, the best way to get the results the organisation actually needs is to keep it simple and comprehensible. If we want quality information we all have to learn to walk before we can run; it is not an easy lesson to learn when the representative from the computer company demonstrates his latest system!

Anyone who has attended any type of computing course will be familiar with the saying 'garbage in—garbage out', referring to the usefulness of information technology. Now that the future of health care organisations in this country may depend even more than ever on getting quality out, we must concentrate on enabling our staff, of whatever discipline, to put that quality in themselves.

8 The internal market—can quality stand the competition?

The year 1991 saw the introduction of a competitive environment for health care. Beyond the 'bottom line' facts and figures of service agreements or contracts, we must concern ourselves with how to contract for the hitherto immeasurable or at least, unmeasured, elements of patient care. These are the elements which we have discussed in this book and which many people feel will suffer in the cut and thrust of the internal market.

It has certainly become clear in the months since April 1991 that survival is the name of the game for health care units. Plans for large-scale redundancies and the prospect of poorly used facilities and specialties going to the wall, particularly in London, evidence this. The task for health service managers is to ensure that good quality care in all senses can be a real factor in ensuring survival and not just a 'bolt-on' special offer for inclusion in a glossy brochure.

Different types of contracts may pose different threats to providing quality care: keeping to contracted activity levels and resource ceilings may mean working to minimum standards and under-use of facilities and skills. Cost and volume contracts may encourage increased throughput and shorter lengths of stay in the hospital service without ensuring the necessary back-up in the community. These risks have already been acknowledged (the 'quicker/sicker debate')[12], and the next months, and perhaps years, will demonstrate how, and if, the internal market will work.

The danger for managers grappling with these problems seems to be the temptation to carry the market and business analogy too far. There are already signs that government terminology is shying away from the language of the market-place—'service agreements' are now more common than 'contracts' in department papers. Doubtless the fashion will change again. The tendency to view the patient as the product, however, is growing, no matter what term is fashionable.

The true product of health care should be the patient's well-being, in terms of clinical outcome, personal comfort and satisfaction. It is the cornerstone of the British health service that such an outcome is sought for all people, regardless of place of residence or ability to pay. If competition is not to diminish the quality of this product, all players in the game will have to strive to achieve a balance between the different perceptions of what is good for business: managers will rightly look for efficiency and the most cost-effective service delivery; doctors will have to weigh up the short-term and long-term success of clinical procedures; other clinicians will also have to look at the therapeutic value of their contribution to patient care but all must remember and acknowledge that the patients want to feel better!

Putting quality into the marketing strategy

If marketing successfully involves proving that our service is best, then these varying and valid definitions of 'best' must be built into the strategy. Cost-effectiveness will be an inherent part of the business strategy of any organisation; the things which matter to people as patients, clients and relatives are the remit of quality programmes or strategies.

We have illustrated some ways of building quality into the fabric of the organisation. The crucial element in the competitive environment must be to demonstrate the effect of quality enhancement on the business of health care: the improvement of staff retention; the reduction in complaints about problems with hospital discharge; and shorter waiting times in out-patients. Not everything which improves patient care can be measured like this but we must capitalise on those elements which can.

Competing successfully within the constraints of the developing NHS market will depend on the evidence of good results that people can give us—what people say (complaints, thank you letters) and what people do (referral patterns, staff achievements, contract placements), as well as the traditional measures of activity, epidemiological and demographic data.

Purchasers and the public will see through a glossy marketing approach if it is unsubstantiated by good business sense and the reality of first-hand experience. It has been the purpose of this book to look beyond sound business principles for what matters in health care. This approach may help to avoid some of the pitfalls of the competitive environment: reduced quality of service in favour of increased quantity, and the emergence of differing levels of service.

Good quality care can flourish in the internal market-place, provided that we attempt to define it with the help and expertise of patients, clients and staff themselves, making it our goal to communicate the emerging principles to the public, the purchasers and all the other players in the game. We hope that this book can contribute something to this exercise by describing some practical steps that managers can take towards that goal.

References

1 Brooks, T. *Sunday Times Competition 1989—The Best of Health*. Introduction.
2 Donabedian, A. *The Definition of Quality and Approaches to its Assessment*. Anne Arbor, Michigan, Health Administration Press, 1980.
3 Wilson, C. R. M. *Hospital-wide Quality Assurance—Models for Implementation and Development*. W. B. Saunders, 1987.
4 Maxwell, R. Quality Assessment in Health. *BMJ* 288 12 May, 1984.
5 Brice, J. *Management in Medicine*, 1989.
6 *National Confidential Enquiry into Peri-operative Deaths*. Department of Health.
7 *Report on Confidential Enquiries into Maternal Deaths in the UK*. Department of Health, 1985-87.
8 Mallett, Jane Shifting the focus of audit. *Health Services Journal*, February, 1991.
9 Zarb, G., Raftery, J., Anderson, R. & Hollowell, J. *Patient Satisfaction Survey at St George's Hospital*. Department of Public Health Sciences, SGH Medical School, University of London, 1990.
10 Sargent, J. Knowing your market: Bury/North Manchester general hospitals. NHS hospital market information requirements. *Health Services Journal*, 101 (5238), 24.5.1991.
11 NHSTA (now NHSTD) *Information Management Training Initiative*, 1990.
12 Packwood, P., Keen, J. & Buxton, M. *Hospital in Transition*. Open University Press, 1991.

Bibliography

General

Ovretveit, J. *Quality Health Services*. University of London, Brunel Institute of Organisation and Social Studies 1988.
Oakland, J. S. *Total Quality Management*, Heinemann 1989.
High, David, *Management of Quality*. IHSM 1988.
Working for Patients, Department of Health, HMSO, 1989.

Clinical audit

Shaw, C. *Medical Audit—A Hospital Handbook*. King's Fund Centre, London, 1989.
The Quality of Medical Care: Report of the Standing Medical Advisory Committee. DOH, HMSO, London, 1990.
Williamson, J. *Providing Quality Care*. Health Services Management, Vol. 87, No. 1, 1991.
Audit Commission, *Measuring Quality: The Patient's View of Day Surgery*. Audit Commission, May 1991.

Customer relations

Quick, A. & Winn, L. *User-Friendly Services Guidelines for Managers of Community Health Services*. King's Fund Centre, 1989.
Winn, L. (ed.) *Power to the People: The Key to Responsive Services in Health and Social Care*. King's Fund Centre, 1990.

Patient satisfaction

Dixon, P. & Carr-Hill, R. *The NHS and its Customers Book III. Customer Feedback Survey—A Review of Current Practice*. Centre for Health Economics, York, 1989.

Haire, Georgia *Open to Question. Nursing the Elderly*, August 1991.

Information from Patients as a Management Tool. Empowering Managers to Improve the Quality of Care. Hospital and Health Services Review, April, 1988.

Tapping Patient Satisfaction: A Strategy for Quality Assessment. *Patient Education and Counselling,* December, 1988, pp. 225-233.

Development of a Patient Satisfaction Scale. *Research in Nursing and Health*, RCN, March, 1986, pp. 43-50.

Surveying Patient Satisfaction by Interviewing in Person. *Dimensions in Health Service*, June, 1986, pp. 30-31.

Patient Satisfaction with Primary Medical Care. *Medical Care*, April 26, 1988, pp. 383-92.

Methods for Measuring Patient Satisfaction with Specific Medical Encounters. *Medical Care*, April 26, 1988, pp. 393-402.

What Physicians Should Know about Patient Satisfaction. *American Journal of Medical Science*, May, 1988, pp. 415-17.

Staff satisfaction and development

McGregor, Douglas *Leadership and Motivation*, MIT Press, 1966.

Cole, G. A. *Personnel Management Theory and Practice*. 2nd edition, D. P. Publications, London, 1988.

Cowling, A. G. & Mailer, C. J. B. *Managing Human Resources*. 2nd edition, Edward Arnold, London, 1990.

Flintham, V. *Skills Shortage in Healthcare: A Resource Book*. Manager Institute of Health Services Management, London, 1990.

Physical environment

Audit Commission, NHS *Estate Management and Property Maintenance*. Audit Commission Review, HMSO, 1991.